This book is dedicated to:
"... *you blocks* ...
"... *you stones* ...
"... *you worse than senseless things* ..."
who have joined
the MAD conspiracy
and watched willingly as ...
stab after stab ...
it assassinates:
RIDICULOUS ADS ...
LUDICROUS MOVIES ...
INSIPID TV PROGRAMS ...
to the point where
MADISON AVENUE
has this to say about
MAD'S ARTISTS, WRITERS AND EDITORS:
*"These men think too much ...
therefore are they very dangerous!"*
Read on ...
and you will see what they mean
when they say:

        BEWARE ...

THE IDES OF
MAD

More of William M. Gaines's MAD Humor from SIGNET

WILLIAM M. GAINES'S

THE IDES

OF

Albert B. Feldstein, Editor

 A SIGNET BOOK

Published by THE NEW AMERICAN LIBRARY,
New York and Toronto
THE NEW ENGLISH LIBRARY LIMITED, LONDON

CONTENTS

If you own a Hi-Fi set, you're a lucky individual. If it works, you're even luckier. Because a Hi-Fi set can turn your living room into a veritable Carnegie Hall. It's even better than the real Carnegie Hall because you're never bothered by late-comers, coughers, program-

A GLOSSARY

HIGH FIDELITY—Full, faithful reproduction of recorded sound.

LOW FIDELITY—Porfirio Rubirosa

LOUDSPEAKER—Person who talks while Hi-Fi set is on.

WOOFER—Dog who talks while Hi-Fi set is on.

TWEETER—A shade stronger than tweet.

TUNER—A salt water fish.

BASS—See TUNER

TREBLE—"Elbert" spelled backwards, honoring Elbert J. Stylus, only man to be trapped on a revolving 78 rpm turntable for 24 hours and live.

AMPLIFIER—What you make to burn an ampli.

OHM—Where Hi-Fi fan sets up equipment.

rustlers, and that $4.80 admission charge. What you are bothered by is hum, distortion, surface noise, and that screaming neighbor. In any case, it looks like Hi-Fi is here to stay, and who are we to fight a trend. So, neighbor, get out your ear-plugs, because in this article

GOES Fi

OF HI-FI TERMS

PICKUP—Someone to listen to Hi-Fi records with.

WOW—Listening to Hi-Fi records with loose pickup.

FLUTTER—Reaction during Wow.

RESISTOR—What you should do with loose pickup.

AM—Midnight to Noon.

FM—Initials of Felix Mulvaney, first man to faithfully record the belch of an owl.

DIAMOND NEEDLE—What Hi-Fi guy gets from impatient, marriage-minded girlfriend.

PITCH—What you get from Hi-Fi salesman.

TUBES—They run between New Jersey and New York.

DISTORTION—Happens when you leave Hi-Fi records on radiator.

EAR-CONDITIONING IS ESSENTIAL FOR

Good Hi-Fi equipment is capable of reproducing sounds between 20 and 40,000 cycles. Unfortunately, the human ear is only capable of hearing sounds to about 15,000 cycles.

ENJOYING HIGH FIDELITY SOUNDS

However, dogs can hear sounds between 15,000 and 40,000 cycles! Pictures below taken over several months show Hi-Fi fan becoming conditioned to Hi-Fi sounds...

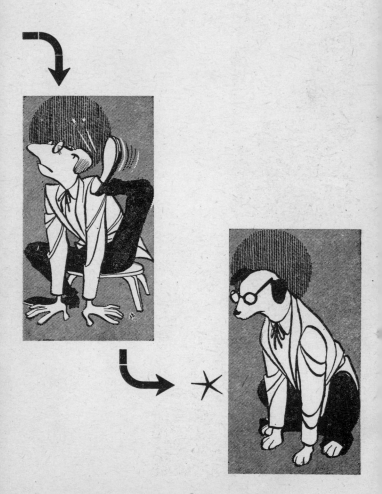

STEP 1: YOUR AMPLIFIER...

Rush out and buy shock-proof, water-proof, anti-magnetic, self-winding, sanforized, cork-tipped, micronite-filtered, "Howling Banshee" 20 Watt Basic Amplifier. Cost: $250.00

STEP 2: YOUR TURNTABLE...

Next, purchase ever-floating, sand-packed, velvet spring, non-neurotic, pre-tranquilized, "Whirling Dervish" X-95, 7-Speed. 4-Shift, 250 Horsepower Turntable. Cost: $125.00

YOUR HI-FI SET

PENSIVE WAY...

STEP 3: YOUR TUNER . . .

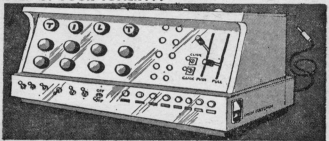

Then order 15-tube, 12-dial, 10-button, 7-switch, 4-light, push-pull, click-click, cross-country, high-strung, over-priced, laminated, "Caramba" AM-FM Tuner. Cost: $150.00

STEP 4: YOUR LOUDSPEAKER . . .

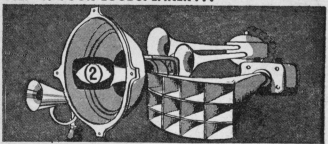

Now shop for birch-faced, six-ply, magic-margin, forward-look, "Little Corporal" Speaker. Cost (including Woofer, Tweeter, Screamer, Shrieker, and Ear-Splitter): $450.00

STEP 5: YOUR REWIRING...

Next step is to rewire your house so you can use all that new Hi-Fi equipment.　Cost of rewiring house: $1500.00

STEP 6: YOUR HIGH-VOLTAGE LINES...

Now you have to erect new high-voltage lines from power plant to carry current needed for house.　Cost: $20,000

STEP 7: YOUR POWER PLANT...

Finally, you have to construct new power plant to produce enough current now needed for house. Cost: $2,000,000

STEP 8: YOUR HEADACHE...

Now you can sit back, listen to Hi-Fi music, and figure out how you're gonna pay for set.   Total Cost: $2,022,475

STEP 1: YOUR AMPLIFIER (AND NEEDLE)...

Scour nearby alleys for mongrel dog with one buck tooth. Plug tail into wall-socket. Output will be surprising! And buck tooth will make fine needle! Cost: Nothing!

STEP 2: YOUR TURNTABLE...

Steal old Lazy Susan Serving-Tray from Dining Room, re-move dishes, cover by gluing down sister's old felt skirt, and drive a ten-penny-nail in the center. Cost: Nothing.

MAD WAY...

STEP 3: YOUR TURNTABLE MOTOR...

Connect turntable to "endless belt" with rope. As howling dog scampers over belt, turntable will revolve. Harness dog's tooth to play LP's.   Cost of "endless belt": $2.00

STEP 4: YOUR LOUDSPEAKER...

Mother-in-law makes dandy loudspeaker, as you well know. Merely connect her up to the mongrel dog. Between them, you'll get all the high and low sounds.   Cost: Nothing!

STEP 5: YOUR CABINET...

Old barrel found in vacant lot serves as fine cabinet for your Hi-Fi set's components.   Cost of barrel: Nothing!

STEP 6: YOUR GOOD FORTUNE...

MAD Hi-Fi set is now finished. You've saved money, and also gotten rid of your Mother-in-law.   Total Cost: $2.00

DISGUISE HI-FI EQUIPMENT TO BLEND INTO DECOR FOR BETTER RESULTS

This can be done in various ways. One method is to hide your Hi-Fi components inside various pieces of furniture.

Another method is to hide speakers through house. This will captivate your friends and family wherever they are.

Your daughter and her fiancé will surely appreciate the sound of romantic Hi-Fi music while necking in the den.

Your week-end guest will certainly get a big kick out of listening to Hi-Fi music while trying to take a shower.

But mainly, disguise your Hi-Fi set's component parts
so your neighbors will have a hard time finding them when

they come calling on you after they've been awakened by
your blasting away at top volume at 2 AM in the morning.

MAD Reviews New Hi-Fi Recordings

Eloquent Elbows

SCHNOOK: *Concerto for Kettledrum and Triangle.* Mischa Goss, soloist. J. Hmphhrich, conducting. Kaput Records, C105, $4.98

NO ONE knows very much about Friedrich Schnook (170?-1?), the German composer who died at the age of seven. We do know that what might have been an impressive career was tragically cut short when the young genius accidentally strangled in the strings of his harp. In any case, his concerto for Kettledrum and Triangle, written when Schnook was six, is a minor masterpiece.

Fortunately for all Schnook lovers, there are 16 versions of this concerto now

reaches new heights in intensity and power, especially during the finale. At that point, Mr. Linseed, who is the only kazoo player in the world with a forked tongue, nearly shatters the speaker with his magnificent crescendo. The disintegration of his wax paper ends the record in a High-Fidelity coup.

Violence in Nature

BATTLE OF THE ANTS: *Sounds of Nature Series, Vol. 3.* Biology Records, MM-53620456794567-J, $5.98

TO MAKE this record, Hamilton Purge lived in an anthill for seven months, waiting for his chance. "Battle of the Ants" is a thrilling, step-by-step narrative in High-Fidelity sound of a bloody war between two ant armies over a lousy

---

Letters To The

MAD HI-FI

Editor

IS IT POSSIBLE?

Dear Hi-Fi Editor,

Is it possible for a printed circuit 40-watt amplifier with an output impedence of 8 ohms and a 70db hum below .35 watts to be connected to a 900 to 20,000 cps 15-omh tweeter with 120° horizontal dispersion and a crossover network of 200 cps when my tuner contains a 3-gang variable condenser, a built-in 20KC whistle filter and three assorted microvolts?

Lance La Touche
Dallas, Texas

It might be fun to try.—Ed.

GURGLING SOUND?

on records. This latest offering is by far the most impressive, and certainly the most complete. Wisely, the performers have not omitted Schnook's famous, but rarely played Elbow Variation in the third movement. This consists of the soloist striking his kettledrums for 15 minutes with his right elbow, and 10 minutes with his left.

This variation will be of particular interest to High Fidelity fans, as the soloist in this performance misses the kettledrum during the 17th minute, and knocks over the podium.

Something New in Beethoven

BEETHOVEN: *Symphony No. 3 (The Eroica) with Kyle Linseed playing the solo kazoo.* Longhair Records, 5-J-322, $3.98

HEARING BEETHOVEN rendered on the solo kazoo makes us wonder if the composer really didn't have this instrument in mind when he wrote his masterpiece. As performed by Mr. Linseed, the symphony

marshmallow. Purge's technical genius has managed to capture all of the marvelous sounds of the conflict . . . the insects' call to battle, the shouts of hand-to-hand combat, the cries of victory, and Purge's own screams when his right forearm is used as a minefield.

For devotees of wildlife sounds, this record set will make a worthy addition to your Hi-Fi library. Also recommended are the other offerings in the Sounds of Nature Series: *"Mating Calls of the Seven Year Locusts",* and *"The Birth of a Water Beetle".*

Sounds of Life

HICCUPS, BELCHES, SNEEZES, AND COUGHS. *Edited by Dr. Bascomb Sneed.* Mucus Records, 2-12" disks, #5007-9, $5.98

TOP NOTCH reproduction, for the most part . . . although several of the belches suffer from distortion. The record jacket boasts that the sneezes (performed by actual hospital patients in wards) are so lifelike, they laid up six audio engineers with bad colds and virus during the recording sessions.

Dear Hi-Fi Editor,

I am puzzled. In Erich Blintze's recording of Brahms 1st Symphony, there is a strange gurgling sound to the trumpets. Is this my set or the recording?
Vladimir Cabot,
Boston, Mass:

It's not your set. This is an example of the new "Seashore Techniques" of Hi-Fi recording where the strings, woodwinds, and percussions play on the beach, and the brass records play underwater.—Ed.

TONE-ARM JUMPS?

Dear Hi-Fi Editor,

Whenever I play a certain LP, my tone-arm jumps. Yesterday, it jumped 12 grooves. Is this the record?
Axel O'Toole,
Flagstaff, Ariz.

No, the record for groove jumping is held by a Dauntless H-13-J tone-arm. On December 4, 1956, it jumped 37 grooves on a record played by Clyde Pincus of Yonkers, N.Y. Sorry.—Ed.

Wake up, America! Before it's too late!
Today our nation is in the grip of a deadly
peril more sinister and diabolical than the

Parking

infamous fifth columns of World War II! These particular columns are made of steel pipe, on top of which are mounted...

Meters

Now, what was that we were doing?

Yes, today, mercenary local officials all over the country, in an effort to fill their city's coffers (and perhaps their own pockets), are innocently destroying America's basic security! They are breaking down its morale! Because the every

Like f'rinstance ...

Now, we here at MAD are all for a guy making a quick buck if he can! But we draw the line when it comes to our country's security. Let's take a look at the handwriting on the

day normal functions of our American way of life are peri-
odically being disrupted by the necessity of our having to
drop everything in order to rush out into the street and put
another coin into that parking meter.

. . . or f'rinstance . . .

wall! Prodded by the success of their "automobile" parking
meters, these mercenary local jerks are gonna keep going!
And before you know it, here's what we'll all be facing!

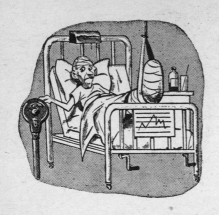

HOVERING METER

RIP

Pretty soon, there'll be so many parking meters for so many different purposes, they'll end up choking

There's only one solution, as we at MAD see it ... the American male must give up driving the family

off all commerce, and "The American Way of Life" as we know it will come to a grinding, sickening halt.

car, and turn that chore over to the women. Given enough time, the menace will certainly be destroyed. **END**

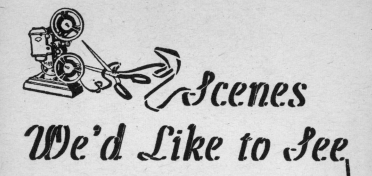

Scenes We'd Like to See

The Beast Falls In Love

END

Today, the great American pastime is endorsing products. It doesn't make much difference what the product is, just so long as the endorser has a big name. In fact, we've found there's hardly any connection at all between the person and the product. These ads will show you what we mean as

Mad

looks at

Endorsements

Star Slugger **MICKEY MANTLE** says:

"ACME Industrial Blast Furnaces are **GREAT!"**

And who should know better than the champion New York Yankee outfielder who is famous for his own mighty blasts. You'll find your plant will hit a "home run" in efficiency every time when you install an ACME Industrial Blast Furnace.

ACME *Only*

$235,000.00 for one
$400,000.00 for two

INDUSTRIAL BLAST FURNACES

Prices slightly higher
west of New Hampshire

43

Arabia's King Ibn Saud says —

"Make Sure it's

SPEEDCO Motor Oil!"

Every time famed Monarch Ibn Saud hops into his air-conditioned limousine to inspect his oilfields, you can bet there's plenty of SPEEDCO Motor Oil in the crankcase! "I never use anything but SPEEDCO," says King Saud, "mainly because I *am* SPEEDCO!"

Only **19c**
per qt. can.

Only **39c**
per filled qt. can.

Rock 'n Roll your Malteds in a
McGillicuddy Mixer

Says ELVIS PRESLEY

Elvis really knows how to shake, rattle and roll...
and that's why he's equipped his home soda fountain
with a McGillicuddy Mixer, the only mixer with a
syncopated beat!

McGillicuddy Mixers

For people who won't take their lumps!

$28⁵⁰ Order regular model for Ordinary A.C.
Order special model for Washington, D.C.

45

"I'm not human!" says

RIN TIN TIN

"But if I were, I'd definitely wear a

FRAMMIS HAT!"

Smart words, we say! Amazingly smart words, in fact, when you realize that dogs can't even talk! All of which proves that anything can happen when you wear a FRAMMIS with its Flip-Top-Brim!*

FRAMMIS HATS

At finer stores in most cities
At lousier stores in all cities

*Patent refused

"I Get Paid to Endorse Nothing!"

says *Alfred E. Neuman*

"Advertisers are scared stiff of me. They know I keep people away and louse up sales. That's why they pay me a fee just to keep my stupid face out of their ads. The last time I endorsed a product, I nearly touched off a national depression. So, if by some chance you happen to see my name on an ad, just forget you ever saw it."

**A Public Service Message from the
NATIONAL ADVERTISING COUNCIL**

END

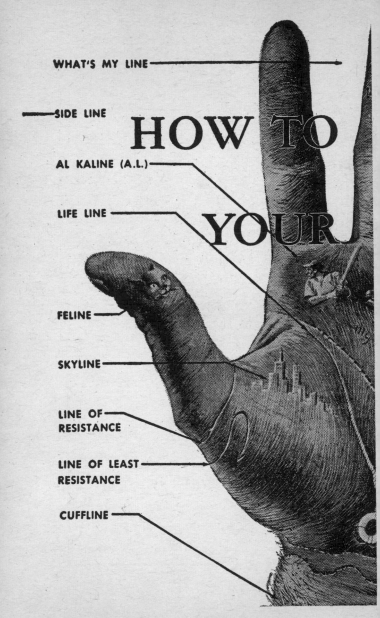

WHAT'S MY LINE

SIDE LINE

HOW TO

AL KALINE (A.L.)

LIFE LINE

YOUR

FELINE

SKYLINE

LINE OF
RESISTANCE

LINE OF LEAST
RESISTANCE

CUFFLINE

48

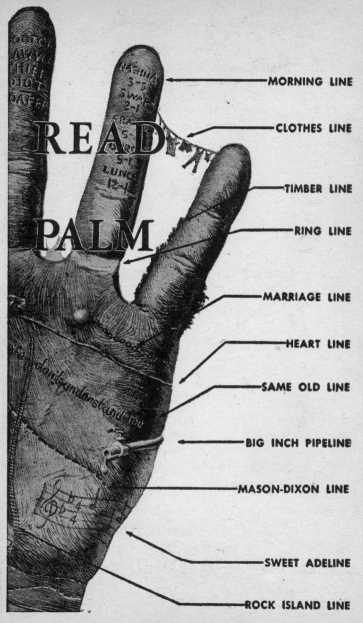

READY PALM

MORNING LINE

CLOTHES LINE

TIMBER LINE

RING LINE

MARRIAGE LINE

HEART LINE

SAME OLD LINE

BIG INCH PIPELINE

MASON-DIXON LINE

SWEET ADELINE

ROCK ISLAND LINE

49

Since the beginning of time, man has been intrigued by the lines in his hand. What do they mean? And how did they get there? Actually, any intelligent two-year-old knows that the lines are caused by folding the hand, and mean nothing. But since most of our readers aren't two years old, *or* intelligent, we're printing this article. Every palm is different, and tells a different story. To the trained eye, the intricate surface of your palm reveals your likes and dislikes, your loves and hates, your accomplishments and goofs, and what you had for breakfast when you wiped off your mouth. So . . .

TYPES OF PALMS

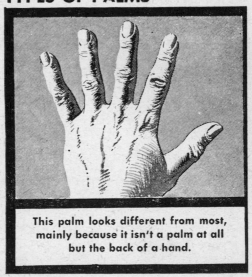

This palm looks different from most, mainly because it isn't a palm at all but the back of a hand.

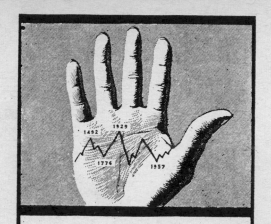

This palm has lines which give important dates in person's life.

This palm gives best dates of all.

WHAT DO CRISS-CROSS LINES MEAN?

The criss-cross lines in the palm tell how successful a person will be in later life. These lines change as a person grows older.

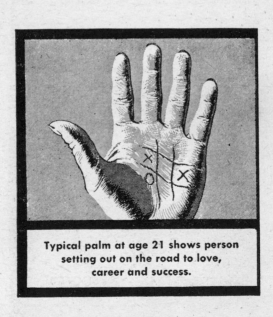

Typical palm at age 21 shows person setting out on the road to love, career and success.

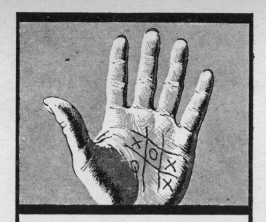

Same palm at age 35 shows person is
well along, has done fine so far.

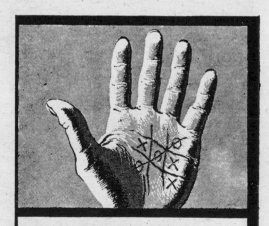

Same palm at age 47 shows person has
lost out, is a complete failure.

WHAT DO WHORLS MEAN?

Whorls are circular patterns set up by lines located at the base of the palm. They accurately tell the occupation of a person.

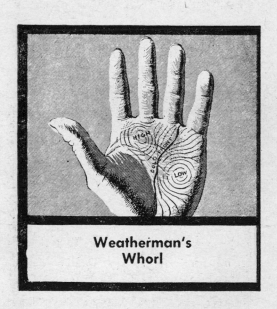

Weatherman's Whorl

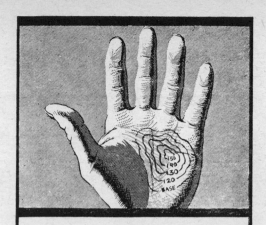

**Mountain Climber's
Whorl**

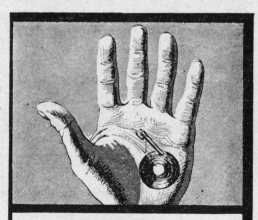

**Disc Jockey's
Whorl**

WHAT DO SHAPES OF FINGERS AND HAND MEAN?

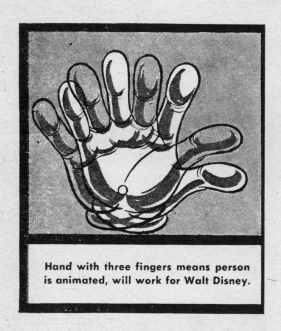

Hand with three fingers means person is animated, will work for Walt Disney.

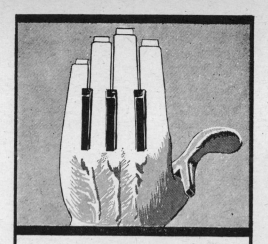

Hand with long, thin fingers means person is artistic, will play piano.

Hand with long, pointing finger means person is Uncle Sam and you'll be drafted!

Hand with fingers in shape of fist
means person is aggressive and
you better duck!

Hand with long curved thumb means
person will travel, mostly in
someone else's car.

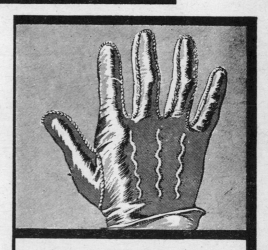

Hand with leathery looking fingers
means person is wearing gloves.

PALMS OF FAMOUS PEOPLE

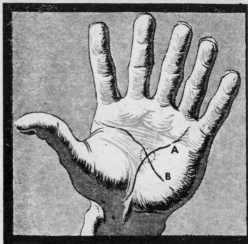

Palm of Alfred E. Neuman is unusual,
has only two lines: lifeline (A),
and mentality line (B).

Detail section of Alfred E. Neuman's mentality line.

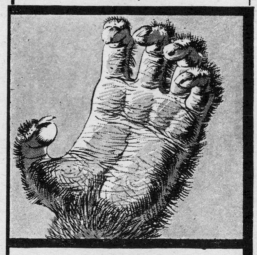

Palm of J. Fred Muggs is not only unreadable, but actually disgusting.

END

KEEP YOUR EYES ON

MAD'S
ENTRANCE

According to all the publicity we've been seeing lately, more students will enroll in colleges and universities this fall than ever before in history, and in an effort to weed out those clods unsuited for higher learning, the entrance exams will be made more difficult. So as a special service we're printing a sample test for MAD readers who plan to go to college. For MAD

UNDERLINE THE PHRASE THAT CORRECTLY COMPLETES THE FOLLOWING STATEMENTS:

1. The Panic of 1837 started because (A) a girl walked down Wall Street in a tight skirt (B) Macy's announced a sale on ladies' hand-bags (C) they found out it was really **1838**.

2. Nero burned Rome because (A) he wanted to set the world on fire (B) they wouldn't let him play his violin at a super-market opening. (C) he liked to see his picture in the papers.

3. In the circulatory system, the aorta carries the blood from the heart because (A) it seems like the thing to do (B) it says so in a Dr. Kildare picture (C) why not?

4. The War of 1812 started because (A) somebody called some-body a slob (B) it was an election year (D) Cecil B. De Mille thought it would be a good idea for a picture.

5. George Washington chopped down the cherry tree because (A) it blocked his view of the window across the way (B) it at-tracted the neighborhood dogs (C) he didn't know how else to get it down.

COLLEGE EXAM

readers who are already *in* college, this test will convince you you don't belong there! For MAD readers who *don't* plan to go to college, this test will convince you you ain't missing a thing! Study questions carefully, then write answer as directed. When you finish, you'll find yourself better prepared to enter that institution. That mental institution.

MATCH UP PERSONS WITH THE DEEDS ATTRIBUTED TO THEM BY INSERTING CORRESPONDING NUMBER IN SPACE PROVIDED:

1. Slugged a headwaiter in El Morocco
2. Posed for nude pictures
3. Writes mash notes to Veronica Lake
4. Has B.O.
5. Once tickled Madame Chiang Kai Shek
6. Handles "hot" jewelry
7. Wrote this article
8. Voted for Alf Landon
9. Doesn't wear underwear
10. Operates a speakeasy in the Bronx

___ Thelonius Monk
___ Marjorie Main
___ Cisco Kid
___ Bronco Nagurski
___ Sabu
___ Bonita Granville's Mother
___ Nick the Gyp
___ Albert B. Feldstein
___ Maria Ouspenskaya
___ Primo Carnera

ASSOCIATION TEST: WRITE DOWN THE FIRST THING THAT COMES TO YOUR MIND WHEN YOU THINK OF THE FOLLOWING:

1. Money
2. Marilyn Monroe
3. Hot skim milk
4. Money
5. Sex

IDENTIFY THESE FIVE GEOMETRIC SHAPES BY UNDER-LINING THE CORRECT DESCRIPTION GIVEN AT RIGHT:

1. (A) a square
    (B) Yul Brynner's head as seen from an airplane
    (C) I don't know

2. (A) a Cataclysmatron
    (B) a photograph of Joe E. Brown taken at his recent opening
    (C) Guy Lombardo as seen by a cool cat.

3. (A) a Whatchamacallit
    (B) a bad drawing of a circle
    (C) the back of a Burma-Shave sign.

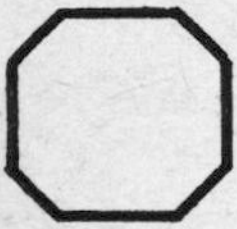

4. (A) a brick wall
    (B) an outline of the state of Idaho
    (C) we can't figure it out either, but our publisher insisted on us inserting it here!

5. (A) a squashed blintz
    (B) a female octopus
    (C) the pancreas of a Malayan jungle lemur

WRITE AN ESSAY OF 250,000 WORDS OR MORE ON ANY THREE OF THE FOLLOWING FIVE TOPICS:

(Use margins of this page)

1. Baseball is ruining our children

2. Why I miss my appendix

3. The last time I felt nauseous.

4. Marching thru Georgia.

5. The most disgusting day of my life.

THE FOLLOWING ARE FIVE PROBLEMS IN MATHEMATICS.
INSERT YOUR ANSWERS ON APPROPRIATE LINE AT RIGHT:
(Use this space for computations)

1. If you only had 96 marbles and needed 100 marbles, how far off your marbles would you be?_____

2. A tank holds 150 gallons of gasoline. The first day, Tom took 3 gallons of gasoline away. The second day, Tom took 12 gallons of gasoline away. How long will it be before they take Tom away?

3. **A** takes 8 hours to pick 12 bushels of apples. **B** takes 14 hours to pick 20 bushels of apples. **C** takes 16 hours to pick 30 bushels of apples. How many bushels would we have if **human beings** were out doing the picking?____

4. John has $10.00. He gives Mary $2.00. How much more will he have to give her before she goes out with him?_____

5. A man takes 4 hours to write 3,000 words by hand. How long would it take him if he used a pencil?_____

ON THE LEFT ARE FAMOUS SAYINGS. MATCH UP THE PERSON
RESPONSIBLE BY NUMBERING THE LINE AT THE RIGHT:

1. "Gee, Dad! A Flexible Flyer!"	___ "Pretty Boy" Floyd
2. "Relax, Baby, you're tense!"	___ Your Esso Dealer
3. "Leggo my arm!"	___ Molly Picon
4. "At 4 A M ? ! ! !"	___ The Piltdown Man
5. Τάδε δέ μοι πάντως, ἔφη, Κροῖσε	___ Fritz Ostermueller
6. "Fresh!"	___ John's Other Wife
7. "Sooo! It's been Max all along!"	___ Melvin Cowznofski
8. "Who's on First?"	___ Gargantua
9. "Eccchhh!"	___ Harpo Marx
10. "Has anyone seen my umbrella?"	___ Tugboat Annie

FILL IN THE MISSING BLANKS TO CORRECTLY
COMPLETE THE FOLLOWING TEN SENTENCES:

1. Alexander Graham Bell invented the telephone because he wanted to call up a girl named _____ in Kansas City.

2. Before Columbus found America in 1492, it was lost for _____ years.

3. The funniest magazine in the world is _ _ _

4. The "E" in Alfred E. Neuman stands for_____
_____

5. The Theory of Relativity means _

6. It was Samuel F. B. Morse who once said •— — •••• — —
— — • •—— ••• ••• — •— •—•

7. Pablo Picasso's latest painting is called ⟍‿⟋⟍

8. The Four Horsemen of the Apocalypse were Melvin, Irving, Morris, and _____.

9. Marilyn Monroe's great talent may be described as ⁀‿

10. Jayne Mansfield's talent may be described as_____‿‿

65

READ THE FOLLOWING TWO SENTENCES (A&B) CAREFULLY THEN ANSWER THE FIVE QUESTIONS THAT FOLLOW EACH:

A. "Low thyroxin causes the rate of oxidation to produce an exophthalmic goiter effecting an oversecretion of tethelin in pituitary anterior lobes manifesting acromegaly while the connected ganglia comprising the autonomic nervous system controlling glandular secretion may accelerate the contractions of the circular muscles of the digestive tract and in all probability produce xerophthalmia".

(From a short poem by Nick Kenny)

1. Wha-a? _____
2. So how come the low thyroxin causes the rate of oxidation to produce an exophthalmic goiter effecting an oversecretion of tethelin in pituitary anterior lobes manifesting acromegaly while the connected ganglia comprising the autonomic nervous system controlling glandular secretion may accelerate the contractions of the circular muscles of the digestive tract and in all probability produce xerophthalmia?
3. Where were you on the night of—OOPS—wrong question—please ignore and go on to number 4.
4. Go back to number 3—it's a funnier question.
5. What does the word "nervous" mean?_____

66

B. "John loves Mary; Mary loves Bill; Bill can't stand Mary and has a crush on Jane; Jane can't see Bill and only has eyes for Fred; Fred doesn't go for Jane and is crazy about Louise; Louise thinks Harry is a big shnook and really digs Steve; Steve claims it's only platonic with Louise and thinks Shirley is the most; Shirley hates everybody but she might make a go of it with John if he stopped seeing Mary."

(All names have been changed to protect the innocent)

1. Who is Sol making out with?_____
2. What does Zelda see in Phil?_____
3. Do you really feel that Frank should continue seeing Madge?___
4. What's this about David and Herman????_____
5. Should Darryl Zanuck do the picture?_____

DEMONSTRATE YOUR KNOWLEDGE OF FOREIGN LANGUAGES BY TRANSLATING THE FOLLOWING QUESTIONS, THEN MATCHING THEM TO THE PROPER ENGLISH ANSWERS

A. ¿Por que cruza el camino un pollo?

B. Pourquoi les pompiers portent-ils des bretelles rouges?

C. Wer war die Dame mit der ich Sie gestern Nache gesehen habe?

D. Veni, vidi, vici!

1. That was no lady, that was my wife!

2. What, —Me worry?

3. To get to the other side.

4. To keep their pants up!

STATISTICS

On the basis of the 5,879 applicants who were recently given this examination at a leading Midwestern college, the following percentage figures have been compiled by the Editors of MAD, and are now published for the first time.

PERCENTAGE	OUTCOME
2%	Passed
39½%	Failed
18%	Were in the wrong room
12%	Fell asleep during True-False Questions
10%	Forgot to bring a pencil
8%	Asked to leave the room and never came back
6%	Didn't know who Veronica Lake was
3%	Made paper airplanes out of the test
2%	Are still working on it
½%	Thought it was funny
Total 101%	(Some wise guy handed in two papers)

POST-MORTEM DEPT.

And now MAD presents its version of the well-known national magazine that derives its title from the day it goes on sale . . . mainly Tuesday!

The Saturday Evening

PeST

February 30, 1938 15¢

OUR STATE DEPARTMENT—DO WE NEED IT?
By Joseph and Stewart Alsop

Cities of the World: FUNKHOUSER, ILLINOIS

THIS ISN'T EXACTLY WHAT I HAD IN MIND
By Benjamin Franklin

Tugboat Annie Sinks

By DIETRICH DUNSTAN DRIZZLE

Could it be? After all her years at the helm, was Annie about to keel-haul her yardarm?

Annie avasted Mr. Sutphen's outrigger. "Yer a bag of second-hand pizened tripe," she said with a note of sadness.

Apex Selby sat in the lobby of the Umgumtumiaki Hotel overlooking the unpaved main street of Port Aakvikalotl, and glanced over the headlines of the Skagway Gazette.

"I've been an Alaskan ship owner for thirty-seven years, now heading a fleet of seven vessels, the largest of which, the 'Primrose', is ably captained by the only woman pilot on the tundra, Tugboat Annie," he mused, a thick thatch of white hair covering his otherwise bald head.

A heavy form sagged into the chair beside Apex, and the pungent aroma told him without looking up that it was Annie.

"Why ye shark-nosed swivel-eared scabbard-sluthering son-of-a-skinamaroo," said Annie amiably, hitting him in the mouth with a hairy fist.

(Now that we've captured your interest, battle your way through the ads to page 427 where this mess is continued.)

I finally went out to the Martin home after waiting for several days while Pete humorously pretended he didn't want to see me.

I CALL PETE

I had finally consented to interview Pete Martin, and a dozen random thoughts were swirling through my mind as my sleek new Ferrari-41 sport car rolled up the drive of his modest Connecticut home.

I remembered that I had been in Connecticut before, once to do my Pulitzer prize-winning series on Syngman Rhee, and once to buy some smoked head cheese at a Hartford grocery that specializes in such mouth-watering delicacies.

Now, wearing an expensive imported camel's hair sport coat and trim fawn-colored slacks, an ensemble that makes me appear much younger than I am, I

(Continued on page 292)

I asked Pete for a picture, and he gave me this one that he took in Yellowstone Park in 1951.

I was fully prepared to be graciously received, but I never expected anything like the welcome I got.

ON
MARTIN

BY FENWICK OVERSHOT

One Pest editor calls
on another to gain an
interview that only the
Pest would dare print.

Pete reluctantly left his busy desk to show me the door after we had concluded our little chat.

So You Think You Know Craps!

By DOMINIC 'PATSY' SCHMURGEN

Under Rule 5.28 of *The International Code of Crap Shooting and Penny Pitching*, it is clearly stated that "failure of one or both dice to land in a flat and easily readable position upon throwing shall result in a void or 'no-dice' situation." The application of this rule resulted in some confusion in an actual game situation which occurred early last season.

The Golden Dukes and the Market Street Marauders are having a friendly little game in the alley behind Dressendorfer's Pool Hall and Recreation Center. Snake Burnbaum is a $12.00 winner. Trigger Grslx is in for about eight clams. Itchy Twirp is down four bucks. And Poochy Duckgluck is approximately even.

Snake's point is eight, and he repeatedly shouts "Eighter from Decatur" as he prepares to roll. Trigger fades him for two skins, and Pooch takes a piece of that. Itchy is interested in a girl across the alley preparing for bed, and is not participating.

On the first roll, one die lands upward in a six position. The other rolls into an open manhole. Snake retrieves the die, announces that it was a two, and that he's made his point. Trigger and Pooch invoke Rule 5.28, arguing that the dice were not "easily readable." Snake replies that he found the missing die lying flat and easily readable in the sewer. So saying, he picks up all bets and pockets them.

If you had been Pooch or Trigger, what would you have done?

(See Page 7003 for answer)

COL. BROWN & FRIEND

The Perfect Squash

Lieutenant Smith, more than a little impressed with his own military ability after finishing first in his class at O.C.S., was assigned to be an aide to an old-line cavalry officer named Colonel Brown.

The young lieutenant proceeded to change the colonel's entire office system, prefacing each new change with the admonition that "this is the way we do it in the *new* army, sir!"

The wily old veteran maintained silence until one day when the lieutenant announced that he was going to consolidate the "Q" and "R" material in the filing cabinet because there was so little filed under "Q."

"It may be confusing to you at first, sir," the young lieutenant smiled condescendingly, "but this is the way we do it in the new army!"

The old colonel turned from the window with a wry expression on his face and said quietly:

"Ahhh, yer fadder's moustache!"

Ewald Prawn

Answers to

So You Think You Know Craps!

It is true that the missing die lay flat.

But it was not "easily readable" by all of the participants in the game.

Therefore, Pooch sat on Snake, while Trigger carved him up with a switch-blade knife.

You Be The Jury

By LUTHER ZITZLAFF

Stevie was an ex-convict who found that his criminal record hampered his efforts to gain employment. After several weeks of job hunting, he was apparently on the verge of being hired by the J & J Necktie Shortener Co. But before the hiring could take place, Stevie's past prison record was brought to light and his application was rejected. In a fit of pique, Stevie shot and killed the J & J firm's Personnel Manager. He then proceeded to file suit against the State Parole Board.

"I am a pathological criminal and the parole board knew it," he argued. "It isn't safe for me to be on the streets. If I'd been kept in prison where I belong, I wouldn't have gotten into further trouble. I demand that the state immediately put me back in stir."

"He done his time so we sprung him," replied the chairman of the parole board. "I mean, you know . . . wha' c'we do?"

If you were the jury, would you rule that Stevie was entitled to go back to prison?

• • • • • • • • • • • • • • •

Stevie won his case. The jury ruled that since he was now a murderer, he was entitled to return to custody, regardless of the fact that he had completed his previous sentence. He lived happily at the State Penitentiary until he was given the electric chair four months later.
Based on a 1831 Utah Decision.

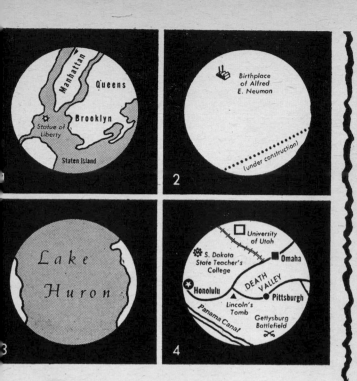

What State Are You In?

...st, West, North or South, each of the distinctive areas above is ...cated in one state. Can you identify what state you are in?

nswer on page xcvii)

Answers to

What State 1. Hysteria   3. Confusion

Are You In? 2. Uncertainty 4. Shock

Eugene Ogg, whose new serial, "WHEATIES, THE BREAKFAST OF CHAMPIONS" begins on page 34, sends along this candid photo of himself at work in his study.

"My wife snapped this from the mouth of our cave with a baby Brownie," Ogg writes. "The baby Brownie is a distant relative on my father's side whom we are raising as our own."

Winston Backrack ("WHY THE COMMUNISTS THINK WE'RE ICKY" in the April 29th Pest) drops us a whimsical note from the big ranch near Woonsocket, R. I., where he and his wife raise albino emus.

"I was shocked to see my article in the Pest," Backrack pens in a fine even hand. "I say it's my article because you lifted the piece word-for-word from 'The American Police Dog' of July, 1954, in direct violation of U.S. Copyright laws."

Backrack fans will be happy to know that his latest article, "I SUED THE PEST AND WON," is now in preparation and will appear shortly.

the Authors

Author Dr. Irving Belknap (STOP PAMPERING YOUR CHILDREN in the May 9th Pest) reports an amazing response to his article. "Three Boy Scout Troops have sworn a vendetta against me," the noted educator writes from an undisclosed hiding place, "and Mickey Mouse Clubs from as far away as Anchorage, Alaska, and the Canal Zone have been sending me cookies containing untraceable poisons."

Seymour Schwab (THE EDGAR LUNDQUIST NOBODY KNOWS in the Jan. 16th Pest) writes from his farm in Desolate, Texas, that a recent tornado there completely destroyed his oil derrick crop.

Mrs. Tillie Eichorn, whose first Pest Fiction, "HONEYMOON IN TEHERAN," appears on page 26, drops us a card from her home near Conway, Ark., to say that she didn't start out to be a writer at all.

"Great balls of fire!" messages Mrs. Eichorn, "All I did was write a letter to Montgomery Ward complaining that the milking stool they sent me wobbles! Imagine my surprise when I learned that my husband had sent the letter to your manuscript editor by mistake, and that it had been accepted for publication as "HONEYMOON IN TEHERAN!"

NEXT WEEK

WE DROVE OUR CHRYSLER TO HONOLULU
A Daring Young Couple, a Carefree
Adventure, a Flooded Motor

NEW YORK FIGHTS BACK
The Story of a Town That Refused To Die

I WAS A CROQUET TRAMP
Is Amateurism Disappearing
From Our Favorite Lawn Game?

YOU DON'T HAVE TO RUN OUT OF SCRATCH PAPER
A Beautiful Portfolio of Eight Blank Pages

CAN THE WHIG PARTY COME BACK?
The Story of a Group Determined To Find
Another John C. Calhoun

THE WHOLE COUNTRY IS GOING MAD
Alfred E. Neuman Threatens To Replace Baseball

Each year, Congress is asked to approve the designs for hundreds of commemorative stamps. Unfortunately only a few of these are ever authorized for printing and distribution. The rest will never feel the wet side of a tongue. But we at MAD have made a hobby of collecting these rejects, and to all you philatelists (and people who collect stamps) we offer now some commemorative issues that have found their way into MAD's

COMMEMORATIVE

STAMP

ALBUM

200TH ANNIVERSARY
1758   1958

3¢

FIRST
UNSUCCESSFUL STEAMBOAT

WHAT---ME WORRY?

Emotionally
Disturbed ★
Youth Week
March 13-20 ★

0¢

THE AMERICAN BAGEL

HONORING

INDUSTRY

2 FOR 5¢

First Railroad Bridge
Without Supporting Posts

$1   Tough Luck 1858 $1

Mid-
Summer
Suit Riot
ROBERT
HALL

$29.95

2053

Honoring the American
Thoroughbred Horse

$25.00 Postage Due
Sorrel

2,000,000th Anniversary
Invention of the Wheel

3¢ Edmund U. Ab 3¢

Charlie Engle Bowls 193. Jan. 14, 1958

4 C Nice Going. Charlie. 4 C

2068

Melvin Cowznofski's
43rd Birthday

10 c.
Black and Blue

30th ANNIVERSARY of the
LAST STEARNS-KNIGHT

$3

GW

Get a Horse

Bicentennial
of First Coal Mine in U.S.

3 1758-1958 3

ONE HECK OF A SWELL GUY

3¢

SANFORD L. KNOEDEL

TRI-CENTENNIAL
1658-1958   2¢

DEATH
OF THE LAST DODO

SESQUICENTENNIAL
PFEIFFER'S POLLY
1808-1958

6¢

2046

National
Hot Rod Week

30 c. Special Delivery
Flash Gray

♠ Honoring the Rogers, Ark.,
Thursday Bridge Foursome.

2¢

♦ Mabel, Grace, Fern, Edna ♥

2067

25th Anniversary of
the End of Prohibition

25 c.
Burgundy

OLD CACHE OF FIREWORKS IN GARAGE
ED HUBER FINDS
SO LONG ED
3¢

Honoring The Nation's Marijuana Growers
3¢ Cool, Man-Cool 3¢

2062
National
Chihuahua
Week
½ c. Beige

J. R. Otwell Fails to Invent Air Brake
1858 – Too Bad, J. R. – 1956
3¢

FRANCINE
LA FLESHE
ME 3-2794
3¢

END

Leave us face it! Man is an argumentative, belligerent animal who, down through the ages, at the drop of a

HOW TO

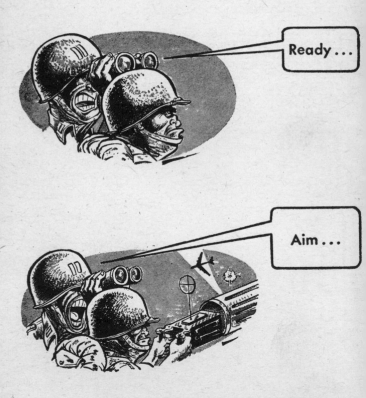

hat, goes to war with his fellow man. So here is MAD's suggestion for a new approach to this age-old problem:

WAGE PEACE

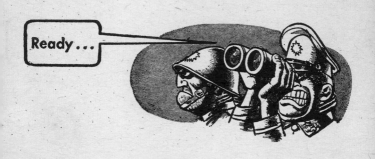

Now you've got the general idea. We figure that as long as men must fight, let them fight in a harmless way . . . a sort of "peaceful war". Since armies consist of people,

they could use the people's games, with the U.N. acting as judge and scorekeeper. Then, to the victors would go the spoils, and nobody gets hurt . . . much. F'rinstance . . .

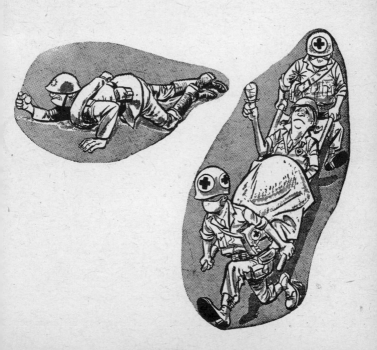

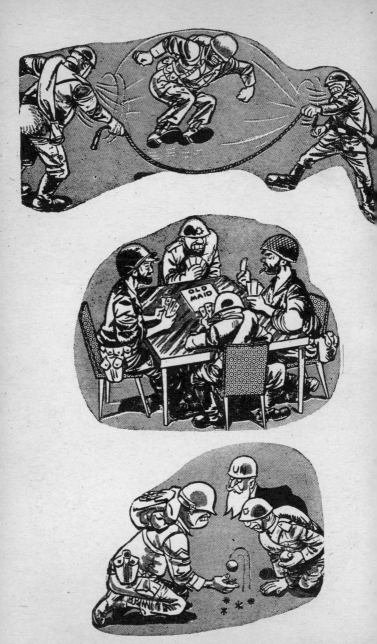

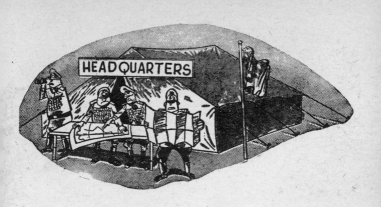

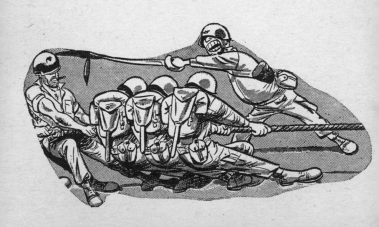

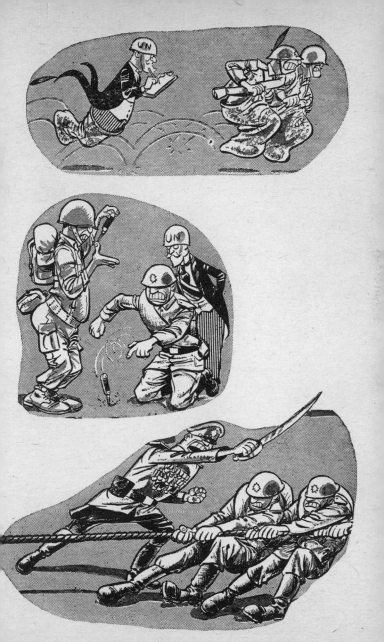

And now, the games of our "peaceful war" are coming to a close. On the Hop-Scotch match rests the entire outcome.

Like we said in the beginning, man is an argumentative, belligerent animal who, at the drop of a hat, goes to . . .

THE PAUSE THAT DEPRESSES DEPT.

You know what's wrong with old movies on TV? Nothing's wrong with them! What's wrong is *the commercials!* They keep getting in the way! TV stations have it worked out so every time the action gets good and the suspense builds up...WHAMMO!...they interrupt with a 2-minute plug for "Soggies, The Pre-Creamed

TV

with

COM

Corn Flakes" or "Uncle Herman's Instant Halvah." By the time
they get back to the movie, you've forgotten what's going on!
   We've got a simple plan to end all these interruptions. And
since every movie winds up on TV eventually, Hollywood could
do well to adopt this plan. Plan being: *Make the commercials a
part of the action itself!* Can't you just see these . . .

MOVIES

built-in

MERCIALS

THE WAR MOVIE

THE JUNGLE MOVIE

THE WESTERN MOVIE

OUTSTANDIN

The Fir

ARTHU

From Garage Mechan

Young "Art" first came before the public eye in 1934 during a demonstration of the new Packard H-47 engine.

AMERICANS

In A Series

A. FREEN

to Automotive Genius

Freen suggested that greater speed could be attained by
simply connecting the cam toggle to the litter bolt-head.

Packard engineers watched in awe as the young mechanic made the proper adjustments for his revolutionary idea.

Any other man would have been discouraged by this sound defeat . . . but not Freen. To him, this was a challenge!

Only a few months later, Arthur Freen came forth with a plan for hooking a Biddle stabilizer to the axle stead.

It was because of Arthur Freen's startling demonstration of this revolutionary new idea on September 28, 1934 . . .

. . . that Studebaker discarded the idea once and for all.

Two years later, Arthur Freen returned to the limelight, this time with a car which he claimed would do 180 MPH.

"All I did was widen the spindle shaft," announced Freen. (An idea Chrysler had been working on for six months!!)

Needless to say, Chrysler immediately gave up the idea!

In 1940, when General Motors decided that more horsepower would result if the breaker gasket were enlarged . . .

It was Arthur Freen who proved conclusively it wouldn't!

Then, as time went by, little was heard from Arthur A.
Freen. Only once . . . some ten years later, in Kokomo . . .

... and again, a few years after that, in Chattanooga ...

Until late in 1957, when Arthur A. Freen, automotive genius, appeared once again with a revolutionary idea . . .

D. MARTIN

END

Many people have difficulty understanding the plays of William Shakespeare because the language they're written in is old-fashioned. Now, for the first time,

SHAKES
UP-TO

MARC ANTONY'S
JULIUS CAESAR

THE OLD VERSION

Friends, Romans, countrymen,
Lend me your ears;
I come to bury Caesar, not to praise him.
The evil that men do lives after them;
The good is oft interred with their bones;
So let it be with Caesar. The noble Brutus
Hath told you Caesar was ambitious;
If it were so, it was a grievous fault,
And grievously hath Caesar answer'd it.
Here, under leave of Brutus and the rest,—
For Brutus is an honorable man;
So are they all, all honorable men,—
Come I to speak in Caesar's funeral.
He was my friend, faithful and just to me;
But Brutus says he was ambitious;

the youth of America can fully appreciate the beauty and significance of his works as MAD, in its campaign to bring culture to all, presents ...

PEARE
-DATE

FUNERAL ORATION
ACT III   SCENE II

THE MAD VERSION

Friends, Romans, hipsters,
Let me clue you in;
I come to put down Caesar, not to groove him.
The square kicks some cats are on stay with them;
The hip bits, like, go down under;
So let it lay with Caesar. The cool Brutus
Gave you the message Caesar had big eyes;
If that's the sound, someone's copping a plea,
And, like, old Caesar really set them straight.
Here, copacetic with Brutus and the studs,—
For Brutus is a real cool cat;
So are they all, all cool cats,—
Come I to make this gig at Caesar's lay down.
He was my boy, the most and real gone to me;
But, like, Brutus pegs him as having big eyes;

And Brutus is an honorable man.
He hath brought many captives home to Rome,
Whose ransoms did the general coffers fill;
Did this in Caesar seem ambitious?
When that the poor have cried, Caesar hath wept;
Ambition should be made of sterner stuff;
Yet Brutus says he was ambitious;
And Brutus is an honorable man.
You all did see that on the Lupercal
I thrice presented him a kingly crown,
Which he did thrice refuse; was this ambition?
Yet Brutus says he was ambitious;
And, sure, he is an honorable man.
I speak not to disprove what Brutus spoke,
But here I am to speak what I do know.
You all did love him once, not without cause;
What cause withholds you then to mourn for him?
O judgement! thou art fled to brutish beasts,
And men have lost their reason. Bear with me;
My heart is in the coffin there with Caesar,
And I must pause till it come back to me.

And old Brutus is a real cool cat.
He copped a lot of swinging heads for home,
Which put us way out with that loot;
Does this give Caesar big eyes?
When the square cats bawled, Caesar flipped;
Big eyes should be made of more solid *megillah*,
Yet Brutus pegs him as having big eyes;
And Brutus is a real cool cat.
You all dug that bit at the Lupercal scene
Three times I bugged him with the King's lid,
And three times he hung me up; was this big eyes?
Yet Brutus pegs him with big eyes;
And, sure, he is a real cool cat.
I don't want to double-O what Brutus gummed,
But, like, I only dig what comes on straight.
You all got a charge out of him once,
So how come you don't cry the blues for him?
Man! You are real nowhere,
You don't make it anymore. Don't cut out on me;
My guts are in the pad there with Caesar,
And I gotta stop swinging till they round-trip.

END

TWINKLE TWINKLE DEPT.

We recently were thumbing through a dusty astronomy book. After we'd put it down, we discovered we knew two things: 1. Ancient astronomy is very dull! And 2. Our thumbs were dusty! Nowadays, constellations are behind the times. No-

MAD'S UP-

ANCIENT CONSTELLATION

ORION The Hunter

body's brought the sky up to date. So we've decided to modernize the whole shebang. On these and the following pages you'll see some redesigned ancient constellations, which is to say, it's a cool sky now, man!

TO-DATE SKY

UP-TO-DATE CONSTELLATION

M A N T L E The Slugger

CANIS MAJOR The Great Dog

CANIS VICTOR The RCA Dog

CASSIOPEIA The Lady In The Chair

MISS AMERICA The Gal On The Throne

D R A C O The Dragon

O L L I E The Dragon

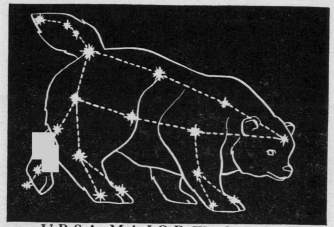

URSA MAJOR The Great Bear

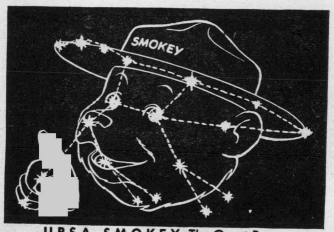

URSA SMOKEY The Great Bear

CYGNUS The Swan

CONSTELLATION The Constellation

LEO The Lion

SPORTY The Speeder

POTRZEBIE
The Polar Star

ALFRED
The Whatmewarry

OSCAR
The Statue

AVA
The Chicken

ELSIE
The Cow

WILLIE
The Penguin

ABNER
The Hillbilly

MOON
The Moon

END

143

Comic Book Publishers! Stop looking for ideas in your rival's comic books and pay attention! This article is for you! Here, for free, is the answer to all your problems: MAD feels, is simple. This is an age of realism! Real realistic realism! "Super Heroes" just aren't realistic! Today, the Comic Book Industry must create "new" heroes.

REALISTIC

HER

MAD's plan to revive the Comic Book Industry. Ten years ago, all our friends were reading about "Super Heroes." But now, they seem to have lost interest. And the reason, These "new" heroes must come from everyday life. Heroes like you and me, leading simple everyday lives and fighting simple everyday crimes. Like, f'rinstance, these ...

COMIC BOOK
OES

149

150

END

Scenes We'd Like to See

The Human Shield

END

DO NOT FEED OR ANNOY DEPT.

A MAD exclusive! For the first time anywhere here is the famous document (partially reproduced for security reasons) from the Martian flying saucer that landed here, inadvertently, a few days ago. (You mean you didn't hear about it?!)

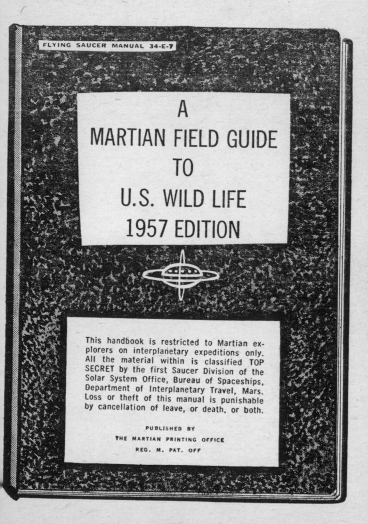

FLYING SAUCER MANUAL 34-E-7

A MARTIAN FIELD GUIDE TO U.S. WILD LIFE
1957 EDITION

This handbook is restricted to Martian explorers on interplanetary expeditions only. All the material within is classified TOP SECRET by the first Saucer Division of the Solar System Office, Bureau of Spaceships, Department of Interplanetary Travel, Mars. Loss or theft of this manual is punishable by cancellation of leave, or death, or both.

PUBLISHED BY
THE MARTIAN PRINTING OFFICE
REG. M. PAT. OFF

THE SCHOLARSHIPUS ATHLETUS

SILHOUETTE

LOOK FOR

This muscular creature can be found crouched on all fours in large circular arenas on Saturday afternoons in the fall. There, to the sounds of primitive chants, he goes through a series of violent lunges and falls. At other times of the year, he can be found on U.S. highways driving a late-model convertible. On rare occasions, he can be observed in the back row of a college classroom, usually with a highly developed case of laryngitis. In later years, he turns into a **Professionalus Athletus,** the only difference being that he has changed his habitat, and now owns **two** late model convertibles.

THE SALTUS SHORELEAVUS

Although the **Saltus Shoreleavus** spends most of his time on the water, he is fascinating to study when he reaches land. Through some mysterious instinct, he can immediately discover where to find an abundance of feminine wildlife. He does his best work when accompanied by a fellow **Saltus Shoreleavus,** or "buddy", who helps him avoid his deadly enemy, the **Saltus Shorepatrolus.** Members of the **Saltus** species readily adapt to all seasons, changing their coloring from blue in winter to white in summer. Strangely enough, his life span usually lasts but four years, after which he molts and turns into the common **Civilianus Salari.**

SILHOUETTE

LOOK FOR

THE LUSHUS EXTREMUS

SILHOUETTE

LOOK FOR

Pictured above is the only known U.S. mammal which feeds entirely on liquids. Noted for his reddish coloring, he can be found perched on high stools in dark, man-made caverns called "bars". There, each evening, before a white-coated attendant, he performs a weird rite known as "pouring out his troubles", which often leaves him in a state of great thirst. (A note of warning!) At times the **Lushus Extremus** becomes extremely hostile. In this state, he should be approached with great caution and only if you are sober and twice his size.

THE CAMPAIGNUS POLITICUS

An intriguing species, the **Campaignus Politicus** has to be seen to be believed, and sometimes can't be believed when seen. He spends most of his time in large meeting places arguing or dozing with others of his breed. In even numbered years, a remarkable transformation occurs. The **Campaignus Politicus** returns to his native haunts where he makes self-laudatory speeches to whoever will listen. During this uninhibited period, he finds himself paternally attracted to babies, housewives, farmers, business men, laborers...everyone! When he leaves public office, he immediately writes a dull book of memoirs, and then turns into a respected **Statesmanus Elderus.**

SILHOUETTE

LOOK FOR

THE SUBURBUS COMMUTERUS

SILHOUETTE

LOOK FOR

This strange mammal is torn between life in the city and life in the country. Because of this, he performs a unique type of daily migration known as "commuting". Since the **Suburbus Commuterus** is a vulnerable species, he protects himself by blending in with the colors of his fellow creatures. Oddly, this blending affects his mind, resulting in a strange manner of speech called "Madison Avenuese". The **Suburbus Commuterus** has one great fear, which he calls "the high cost of living". He fights this dire economic threat through a novel means of self-preservation known as "the expense account".

THE SUBURBUS DOMESTICUS

The **Suburbus Domesticus** behaves totally unlike her mate. To begin with, she does not fear "the high cost of living"; instead she helps boost it through a local ritual known as "keeping up with the Joneses". This is mainly done through an activity called "the buying spree" which occurs instinctively whenever she feels she has been cooped up too long. The **Suburbus Domesticus** does not believe in identical colorings, and goes to great lengths to avoid sporting the same plumage as her neighbor. In later years, she carefully watches her mate's health, and often examines his white collar for red marks, which are sure signs of the dreaded **Sweetheartus Outsidus** disease.

SILHOUETTE

LOOK FOR

THE SNOBBUS SOCIETUS

THE IDOLUS BOBBYSOXUS

Although the **Snobbus Societus** is slowly becoming extinct, the few remaining are endowed with great power, compensating for a brain which is remarkably small. She is a durable creature, whose sole purpose in life is to outlive the others of her species. She can be observed in her native habitat — a large and decaying dwelling in the older section of a large city. There, the **Snobbus Societus** is frequently surrounded by a bevy of chattering **Socialus Climbus**, who feed on her ego. This strange diet often affects the color of her blood, which allegedly turns dark icy blue.

Of all U.S. mammals, none has a larger following than the **Idolus Bobbysoxus**. He produces a variety of sounds which bring forth eerie shrieks and moans from his followers, usually made up of thousands of young U.S. earthwomen. He is particularly noted for well-developed body movements, which often prevent his audience from listening to the sounds he emits. No one has ever been able to discover what happens to the **Idolus Bobbysoxus** once he has been replaced by a much younger **Idolus Bobbysoxus**.

SILHOUETTE   LOOK FOR

SILHOUETTE   LOOK FOR

THE BLONDUS IGNORAMUS

SILHOUETTE

LOOK FOR

Most U.S. creatures are self-sufficient. The **Blondus Ignoramus**, however, has no means of self-preservation and must live off others. At an early stage of life, she finds it impossible to feed or clothe herself in the manner to which she'd like to be accustomed. When this happens, she is taken under the wing of another remarkable creature, the **Tycoonus Sugardaddyus.** At the same time, her natural coloring — a dull brunette — miraculously changes to flashly blonde. It should be carefully noted that the **Blondus Ignoramus** never reaches the age of more than 29 years.

THE TYCOONUS SUGARDADDYUS

Although an aging beast, the **Tycoonus Sugardaddyus** usually reverts to his youth by a ritual known as "turning back the clock". When this happens, he finds that he has a strong attraction for the **Blondus Ignoramus**, and spends the last years of his life in this interesting pursuit. Since he imagines himself a much younger creature, he enjoys being called infant-like names such as "Snookums" or "Cuddles". He earns these titles of respect through a variety of means, mainly expensive gifts, two of which are the mink coat and the diamond necklace.

SILHOUETTE

LOOK FOR

END

The Russians, who have a habit of giving us problems, gave us a dilly when they launched Sputnik and Muttnik . . . problem being: what to do about the dangerous shortage of scientists here in America? It seems that most kids today choose careers where they can make **money** rather than

HOW TO MAKE

SCIENCE

careers where they can use their **brains**. So,
because we all made the same mistake, the
staff of **MAD** suggests that an all-out effort
be started by the Press, Television, and
Movies to arouse the interests of America's
teen-agers in science and careers in science.
Here, then, is **MAD's** own plan on...

AMERICA'S KIDS...

CONSCIOUS

THE TV WESTERN

Yuh see, when the hammer of mah .45 struck this primer, here, it set off some fulminite which ignited the gunpowder packed inside the cartridge case. The resultant heat and expanding gases forced the bullet from the case, projected it down the barrel, and into the critter's belly.

Then . . . thanks to **heat** and **expanding gases**, we still got law and order in Redstone!

Yep! That . . . and mainly 'cause I also **outdrew 'im!**

THE SPORTS INTERVIEW

174

THE CRIME MOVIE

THE COMIC STRIP

THE GIRLIE SHOW

END

There is nothing as inspiring as a poem...
unless it happens to inspire Don Martin!
F'rinstance here is his interpretation of

WOODMAN, SPARE THAT TREE!

by George Pope Morris

Woodman, spare that tree!
Touch not a single bough!

10

11

END